Published by Ravette Publishing 2004
Copyright © 2004 United Feature Syndicate, Inc.
All rights reserved.
Licensed by PSL
(www.snoopy.com)

PEANUTS is a registered trademark of
United Feature Syndicate, Inc.
Based on the PEANUTS® comic strip
by Charles M. Schulz.

Printed and bound in Great Britain
for Ravette Publishing Limited,
Unit 3, Tristar Centre,
Star Road, Partridge Green,
West Sussex RH13 8RA

by Cox & Wyman, Reading, Berkshire.

ISBN: 1 84161 196 4

MY THIRD
2 in 1 COLLECTION
CONTAINS:

THE LEGAL BEAGLE
THE GREAT PHILOSOPHER

SNOOPY

features as

The Legal Beagle

Charles M. Schulz

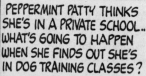

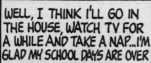

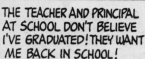

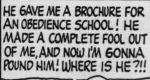

I'VE READ A LOT ABOUT ABRAHAM LINCOLN WHEN HE WAS AN ATTORNEY...

NOT ONCE, ON THE DAY OF A TRIAL, WAS HE UNABLE TO FIND THE COURTHOUSE

LIFE WAS SIMPLER THEN!

12-2

THE COURT WILL NOT AID THOSE WHO HAVE COMMITTED ILLEGAL ACTS IN A MATTER...

..AND THEN ASK THE COURT'S HELP TO RECOVER FOR ANY INJURY THEY MAY HAVE SUFFERED AS A RESULT THEREOF!

12-3

RATS!

© 1982 United Feature Syndicate, Inc.

SNOOPY

features as

The Great Philosopher

Charles M. Schulz

ℛℛ

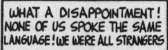

CHOMP
CHOMP
CHOMP

HERE YOU ARE, SNOOPY...
YOU CAN HAVE THE REST
OF MY DOUGHNUT...

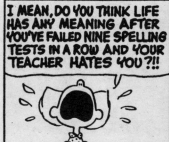

2-13

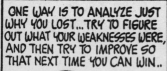

I RECOGNIZE THAT KICK...THAT'S THE KICK OF SOMEONE WHO HAS AWAKENED IN THE MIDDLE OF THE NIGHT, AND WANTS TO KNOW THE MEANING OF LIFE...

PEANUTS

IN THE ENTIRE HISTORY OF THE WORLD, THERE'S NO RECORD OF SANTA CLAUS EVER FILLING THE STOCKING OF A BIRD...

BUT THAT DOESN'T DISCOURAGE WOODSTOCK..

12-22

HE FEELS THE ODDS ARE WITH HIM!

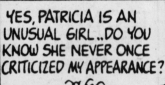

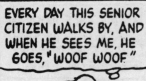

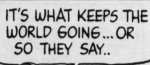

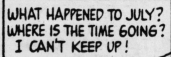

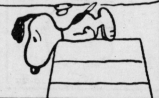

3-18

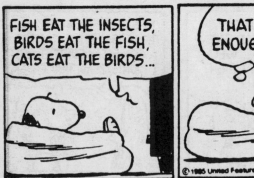

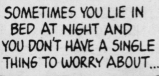

THAT'S STRANGE..I FEEL LIKE I'VE SEEN THAT DOG BEFORE..

ISN'T THERE AN EXPRESSION FOR THAT?

DÉJÀ BEAGLE!

SOMETIMES, IF YOU PURPOSELY LOOK SAD, THEY'LL BRING YOU AN EXTRA BIG SUPPER...

HI, I NOTICED YOU APPEARED A BIT PEAKED..

I FIGURED YOU PROBABLY WEREN'T FEELING SO GOOD SO I DIDN'T GIVE YOU AS MUCH TO EAT..

7-15

AND SOMETIMES YOU DO SOMETHING THAT IS SO STUPID IT STAGGERS THE IMAGINATION!

Other PEANUTS titles published by Ravette . . .

Pocket Books	ISBN	Price
Man's Best Friend	1 84161 066 6	£2.99
Master of Disguise	1 84161 161 1	£2.99
Master of the Fairways	1 84161 067 4	£2.99
The Fearless Leader	1 84161 104 2	£2.99
The Great Entertainer	1 84161 160 3	£2.99
The Great Philosopher	1 84161 064 X	£2.99
The Legal Beagle	1 84161 065 8	£2.99
The Master Chef	1 84161 107 7	£2.99
The Music Lover	1 84161 106 9	£2.99
The Sportsman	1 84161 105 0	£2.99
The Tennis Ace	1 84161 162 X	£2.99

2-in 1 Collections		ISBN	Price
Book 1		1 84161 177 8	£4.99
Book 2		1 84161 178 6	£4.99
Book 4	(new)	1 84161 197 2	£4.99

Little Books	ISBN	Price
Charlie Brown – Friendship	1 84161 156 5	£2.50
Charlie Brown – Wisdom	1 84161 099 2	£2.50
Educating Peanuts	1 84161 158 1	£2.50
Lucy – Advice	1 84161 101 8	£2.50
Peanuts – Life	1 84161 157 3	£2.50
Peppermint Patty – Blunders	1 84161 102 6	£2.50
Snoopy – Laughter	1 84161 100 X	£2.50
Snoopy – Style	1 84161 155 7	£2.50

Black & White Landscapes	ISBN	Price
Now, That's Profound Charlie Brown	1 84161 181 6	£4.99
I Told You So, You Blockhead!	1 84161 182 4	£4.99

Colour Collections		ISBN	Price
It's A Dog's Life, Snoopy		1 84161 179 4	£9.99
It's A Big World, Charlie Brown	(new)	1 84161 188 3	£9.99

Miscellaneous	ISBN	Price
Peanuts Anniversary Treasury	1 84161 021 6	£9.99
Peanuts Treasury	1 84161 043 7	£9.99
You Really Don't Look 50 Charlie Brown	1 84161 020 8	£7.99

Snoopy's Laughter and Learning	ISBN	Price
Book 1 – Read with Snoopy	1 84161 016 X	£2.50
Book 2 – Write with Snoopy	1 84161 017 8	£2.50
Book 3 – Count with Snoopy	1 84161 018 6	£2.50
Book 4 – Colour with Snoopy	1 84161 019 4	£2.50

All PEANUTS books are available at your local bookshop or from the publisher at the address below. Just tick the titles required and send the form with your payment to:-

RAVETTE PUBLISHING
Unit 3, Tristar Centre, Star Road, Partridge Green, West Sussex RH13 8RA

Prices and availability are subject to change without notice.

Please enclose a cheque or postal order made payable to **Ravette Publishing** to the value of the cover price of the book and allow the following for UK postage and packing:

60p for the first book + 30p for each additional book
except *You Really Don't Look 50 Charlie Brown* when please add £1.50 per copy, *It's A Dog's Life, Snoopy* and *It's A Big World Charlie Brown* please add £2.50 p&p per copy and the two *Treasuries* – please add £3.00 p&p per copy.

Name ....

Address ....

....

....

....